What's happening?

At the seaside · On the farm · At the zoo

Heather Amery
Illustrated by Stephen Cartwright

Language Consultant: Betty Root

What's happening?
At the seaside

Building a sandcastle

Everyone is doing something to help build the sandcastle.
Who is digging the moat?

Which bucket made the top of the castle?
How many flags are there?

In the sea

How many children are wearing snorkels?
Who is learning to swim?

Who doesn't like being in the water?
How many seagulls are there?

Having a picnic

How many children are eating sandwiches?
Who is wearing sunglasses?

Who is getting cold?
Who is being naughty?

Playing in the rock pool

How many crabs can you see?
Who is about to fall into the water?

How many red buckets are there?
Who is collecting shells?

On the jetty

How many children are fishing?
What has the girl in the striped top caught?

What are the cats waiting for?
Who has lost her hat?

At the ice cream stand

How many birds can you find?
Who has a cold head?

Which children have pink ice creams?
What other kinds can they buy?

Time to go home

Everyone seems to have lost something.
Who is looking for his pipe? Can you see where it is?

Can you help the others find a missing shoe, a paddle,
a sandal, a sock and a flipper?

Getting dressed

Who do all these things belong to?

What's happening?
On the farm

A visit to the hens

Can you see how many eggs the hens have laid?
Who is asleep in the hen house?

Can you name all the animals in the picture?
What is the horse doing?

Shearing the sheep

Sheep need to have their woolly coats cut off in summertime.
Can you see which sheep is being sheared at the moment?

Which animal shouldn't be in the sheep pen?
One lamb is missing from the pens. Can you find it?

Looking at the pigs

How many pigs can you see?
How many are piglets?

Pigs eat from a trough.
Which other animal is looking for food?

Feeding the ducks

Baby ducks are ducklings and baby geese are goslings.
How many of each can you see?

Which duckling is getting a ride?
What other animals can you see around the pond?

Milking time for the cows

Cows need to be milked every day.
Which cow doesn't want to be milked?

Who is going to get wet?
Who is slipping in the mud?

Picking the apples

How many different animals can you see?
How many apple trees are there?

Who is picking apples?
Who is eating them?

By the barn

How many kittens are there?
Find 2 white hens and 3 mice.

What has happened to the trailer?
Who has lost a shoe?

Match the mothers with their babies

What are the baby animals called?

What's happening?
At the zoo

Looking at the animals

Can you find the zoo keeper?
What are they doing?

How many different animals can you see?
Which ones have babies?

Watching the lions

How many lion cubs are there?
Which one is going to get into trouble?

Can you find a white mouse?
What's stuck in the tree?

Looking at the birds

How many different kinds of birds can you see?
Which ones have the biggest beaks?

What do penguins like to eat?
How many birds are swimming?

In the aquarium

Which fish have stripes?
Can you find all the yellow fish?

Do you know the names of all these creatures?
How many people are looking at them?

Bathtime for a polar bear

How many cubs are there?
How many children are wearing hats?

Playtime for the dolphins

How many dolphins are there?
Which ones have red rings?

The chimpanzees and the gorillas

Chimpanzees have pale faces and gorillas have black faces.
What are all the chimpanzees doing?

How many baby gorillas can you see?
Which fruits do chimpanzees and gorillas like to eat?

In the children's zoo

How many rabbits can you count?
What other animals can you see?

What are all the goats doing?
Who has lost a shoe?

Animal puzzle

Match the animals' heads with their legs.

First published in 1993, Usborne Publishing, Usborne House, 83-85 Saffron Hill, London EC1N 8RT.
Copyright © 1993, 1992, 1984 Usborne Publishing Ltd.
The material in this book is also available as three separate titles
in the Usborne What's happening? series.

First published in America March 1993

UE